SO-BED-986

by Daphne Greaves
illustrated by Ken Bowser

SCHOOL PUBLISHERS

Printed in China

ISBN 10: 0-15-350502-8
ISBN 13: 978-0-15-350502-7

Ordering Options
ISBN 10: 0-15-350333-5 (Grade 3 Below-Level Collection)
ISBN 13: 978-0-15-350333-7 (Grade 3 Below-Level Collection)
ISBN 10: 0-15-357490-9 (package of 5)
ISBN 13: 978-0-15-357490-0 (package of 5)

2 3 4 5 6 7 8 9 10 985 12 11 10 09 08 07

## Characters

| | | |
|---|---|---|
| **Announcer 1** | **Zork** | **Man** |
| **Announcer 2** | **Woman** | **Matt** |

**Setting:** A kitchen on the television show *Cooking with Zork*

**Announcer 1:** Welcome to the show *Cooking with Zork!*

**Announcer 2:** Co-starring Zork's helper, Matt Brown!

**Zork:** Hello to all our friends throughout the universe.

**Matt:** What are we making today?

**Zork:** A delicious razzle cake. This cake was created by inhabitants of the planet Fire!

**Matt:** Where's the fire? I'll put it out!

**Zork:** Put down that hose. Your emotions are running away with you.

**Matt:** What about the fire?

**Zork:** There is no fire. The recipe is from the planet Fire!

**Matt:** Oops! Now for a word from our sponsor!

**Announcer 1:** Sometimes nothing but a decent, home-cooked meal will do. What if you're far from home? Then what do you do?

**Announcer 2:** Go to the Blue Moon Restaurant. Yes, it's on the moon!

**Announcer 1:** Do you want the best chili, hamburgers, or pizza?

**Announcer 2:** Go to the Blue Moon Restaurant, visible from the earth. Only a healthy appetite is required!

**Matt:** Now we're back!

**Zork:** The first time I tasted razzle cake, I was filled with amazement.

**Matt:** Not to mention razzle cake!

**Zork:** It's delicious and takes little effort to make.

**Matt:** Then let's make it!

**Zork:** Take two tablespoons of happiness and one cup of fun. Mix them together.

**Matt:** That smells heavenly.

**Zork:** The first time I smelled razzle cake, I was on Fire!

**Matt:** Don't worry! Here's the fire hose!

**Zork:** Matt, didn't you learn anything from the last time?

**Matt:** Oh, you meant the planet Fire!

**Zork:** As I was saying, the smell of razzle cake beckoned to me.

**Matt:** I can't wait to taste it.

**Zork:** This next ingredient is razzle butter. It's very scarce, so don't use too much. Add four tablespoons. This ample recipe makes enough cake for ten people.

**Zork:** Now we bake it.

**Matt:** After this commercial, we'll see how our razzle cake turned out.

**Man:** Keeping the house clean is a big responsibility.

**Woman:** Get Robo Cleaner, the fully functional cleaning robot. It does all your chores!

**Man:** Thank you, Robo Cleaner.

**Woman:** This man used to clean his house after work.

**Man:** I was permanently tired.

**Woman:** Now he comes home and dozes on the couch or enjoys a good book.

**Man:** I'm so relaxed.

**Woman:** Get Robo Cleaner, and you'll feel relaxed, too.

**Matt:** Welcome back to the show.

**Zork:** We're just taking the cake out of the oven.

**Zork:** I'm melting razzle butter to pour over the cake.

**Matt:** Yum!

**Zork:** Oh, that's hot! Please hand me that potholder.

**Matt:** You bet! May I please have a taste now?

**Zork:** Okay, Matt, close your eyes.

**Matt:** My eyes are closed!

**Zork:** Oh, no! The potholder is on fire!

**Matt:** I'm not falling for that one again.

**Zork:** Get the fire hose!

**Matt:** Ha, ha, ha! What's that smell?

**Zork and Matt:** Fire!

**Matt:** I'm spraying the fire! It's out! Oops!

**Zork:** You got foam all over the cake.

**Matt:** What are we making next week, Zork?

**Zork:** Flaming fajitas!

**Announcer 1:** Tune in next week—

**Announcer 2:** For *Cooking with Zork!*

# Think Critically

1. What was the first commercial for?

2. Why did the man in the Robo Cleaner commercial feel tired?

3. If you could ask Zork a question, what would it be?

4. What is the meaning of the word *required* on page 6?

5. What was your favorite part of this Readers' Theater? Why?

 **Science**

**Planet Poster** Zork is from an imaginary planet. Choose a planet in our solar system and make a poster that includes some facts about the planet you chose.

**School-Home Connection** Talk with a family member about cooking. Discuss what kinds of food you each like and why. Plan to cook something together.

**Word Count:** 534